THE TALE OF BENJAMIN BUNNY

Adapted from the story and art
by Beatrix Potter
Line art by Lisa Wallace

Copyright © 2014 Dalmatian Press, an imprint of Bendon Publishing International, Inc.
Franklin, Tennessee 37068-2068.
No part of this book may be reproduced or copied in any form
without the written permission of Dalmatian Press. All rights reserved.
Printed in Ft Wayne, IN, USA.
CE17990/0913 Super Book to Color - THE TALE OF BENJAMIN BUNNY / THE TALE OF TOM KITTEN

One morning, little Benjamin Bunny sat on a bank.
He heard the trit-trot of Mr. McGregor's carriage.

So, Mr. McGregor was leaving for town! With a hop,
skip, and a jump, Benjamin Bunny set off down the path.

The wood was full of rabbit holes. In the neatest, sandiest hole lived
Benjamin's Aunt and his cousins—Flopsy, Mopsy, Cottontail, and . . .

. . . Peter! But Peter was not at home in the rabbit hole.
Benjamin went looking for him.

Benjamin came round the back of a tree.

Benjamin found Peter dressed in a pocket-handkerchief,
for he had lost his clothes in Mr. McGregor's garden.

Little Benjamin sat down beside his cousin
and told him that Mr. McGregor had gone to town.

And where do you think those two little rabbits set off to?

Dalmatian Press

Mr. McGregor's garden! And there they
saw Peter's coat and shoes on a scarecrow.

Rather than squeeze under the gate, the two cousins
climbed down a pear tree—but poor Peter tumbled down!

They left many little footprints in the soft lettuce bed.

Peter took his clothes from the scarecrow and put them on.
Benjamin tried on the tam-o'-shanter, but it was too big for him.

Benjamin filled the pocket-handkerchief
with onions, as a little present for his Aunt.

Peter did not seem to be enjoying himself.
He kept hearing noises.

But Benjamin said he was in the habbit of
coming to the garden with his father to get lettuces.

And the lettuces certainly were very fine.

Peter did not eat anything. He wanted to go home.
Soon he had dropped half the onions.

Benjamin led the way to the other side of the garden. Little mice sat on their doorsteps cracking seeds and winking at the bunnies.

Presently Peter let the pocket-handkerchief go again.

The cousins got among the flower pots and Peter heard noises!
Suddenly he stopped!

This is what those little rabbits saw around the corner!

In no time at all, little Benjamin and Peter
hid underneath a large basket.

The cat got up, sniffed, and sat right down on top of the basket.
She sat there for *five hours*.

Pitter-patter, pitter patter. Mr. Benjamin Bunny
was on the wall above the shed looking for his son.

Mr. Benjamin Bunny was not afraid of cats.
He pounced onto that cat and kicked it into the greenhouse!

He lifted the basket and got his son Benjamin and his nephew Peter.

Then Mr. Benjamin Bunny marched
those two naughty bunnies out of the garden.

Mr. McGregor returned and thought:
Where did the scarecrow's clothes go?

When Peter got home, his mother forgave him,
because she was so glad to see that he had found his shoes and coat.

THE END

From the World of Beatrix Potter

Jeremy Fisher

Mrs. Tiggy-Winkle

Peter Rabbit

MRS. RABBIT

Peter Rabbit

THE TALE OF TOM KITTEN

Adapted from the story and art
by Beatrix Potter
Line art by Lisa Wallace

Dalmatian Press

Once upon a time there were three little kittens,
and their names were Mittens, Tom Kitten, and Moppet.

One day their mother, Mrs. Tabitha Twitchit, brought them inside
to wash and dress, for she was expecting company for tea.

First she scrubbed their faces (this one is Moppet).

Then she brushed their fur (this one is Mittens).

Then she combed their tails and whiskers (this is Tom Kitten).
Tom was very naughty, and he scratched.

Mrs. Tabitha dressed Moppet and Mittens in clean pinafores and tuckers.
Then she found some elegant (but uncomfortable) clothes for Tom.

Tom Kitten had grown plump, and several buttons burst off.
His mother sewed them on again.

Mrs. Tabitha sent her kittens to the garden.
"Now, keep your frocks clean, children.
And keep away from Sally Henny-Penny and the Puddle-Ducks."

As Moppet and Mittens walked down the garden path,
they tripped on their pinafores and fell on their noses.
When they stood up there were several green smears!

"Let us climb through the rock garden and sit on the wall," said Moppet.
So they turned their pinafores around and jumped up.
Moppet's white tucker fell down into the road.

Tom Kitten came through the rockery bit by bit, breaking the ferns, and shedding buttons right and left.

He was all in pieces when he reached the top of the wall.
Moppet and Mittens tried to pull him together, but his hat fell off,
and the rest of his buttons burst.

Along came a pit pat, paddle pat! The three Puddle-Ducks
came along the road, marching with a pit pat, paddle pat!
Pit pat, waddle pat!

They stopped and stared up at the kittens.
They had very small eyes and looked surprised.

Then Rebeccah and Jemima Puddle-Duck picked up
the hat and tucker and put them on.

Mittens laughed so that she fell off the wall.
Moppet and Tom tumbled after her.
The pinafores and all the rest of Tom's clothes came off on the way down.

"Come! Mr. Drake Puddle-Duck," said Moppet.
"Help us to dress and button up Tom!"
And so Mr. Drake Puddle-Duck picked up Tom's clothes . . .

. . . but he put them on himself!
They fit him even worse than Tom Kitten.
"It's a very fine morning!" said Mr. Drake Puddle-Duck.

And he and Jemima and Rebeccah Puddle-Duck set off up the road.
Pit pat, paddle pat! Pit pat, waddle pat!

Then Tabitha Twitchit came down the garden and found her kittens on the wall with no clothes on.

She pulled them off the wall and gave them a firm pat.
"My friends will arrive in a minute," she said, "and, oh, you are not fit to be seen!"

She sent them upstairs. And I am sorry to say she told her friends
that they were in bed with the measles—which was not true.

Quite the contrary. They were not in bed—*not* in the least.
Somehow there were very bumpity noises overhead,
which disturbed the rather prim and proper tea party.

And I think that some day I shall have to make another,
larger, book, to tell you more about Tom Kitten!

As for the Puddle-Ducks, they went into a pond.
The clothes all came off, of course, because there were no buttons.

And Mr. Drake Puddle-Duck, and Jemima, and Rebeccah,
have been looking for them ever since.

THE END